Saint Francis of Assisi

Messenger of Peace

Written by Toni Matas

Illustrated by Picanyol

Color by Carlos Rojas

Pauline
BOOKS & MEDIA
Boston

CANTICLE OF THE SUN

MOST HIGH, ALMIGHTY, GOOD LORD,
PRAISE, GLORY, HONOR, AND BLESSING ARE ALL YOURS,
TO YOU ALONE DO THEY BELONG.
NO ONE IS WORTHY TO MENTION YOUR NAME.

BE PRAISED, MY LORD, WITH ALL YOUR CREATURES . . .
ESPECIALLY TO BROTHER SUN, THROUGH WHOM YOU GIVE US
THE LIGHT OF DAY. HE IS BEAUTIFUL AND RADIANT WITH GREAT
SPLENDOR. HE IS SIMILAR TO YOU, MOST HIGH!

BE PRAISED, MY LORD, FOR SISTER MOON AND THE STARS! IN THE
HEAVENS YOU FORMED THEM, CLEAR, PRECIOUS, AND BEAUTIFUL.

BE PRAISED, MY LORD, FOR BROTHER WIND AND FOR THE AIR, CLOUDY AND CLEAR, AND EVERY KIND OF WEATHER, BY WHICH YOU GIVE NOURISHMENT TO YOUR CREATURES.

BE PRAISED, MY LORD, FOR SISTER WATER, WHICH IS VERY USEFUL, HUMBLE, PRECIOUS, AND PURE.

BE PRAISED, MY LORD, FOR BROTHER FIRE, BY WHOM YOU LIGHT THE NIGHT; HE IS BEAUTIFUL, MIGHTY, AND STRONG.

BE PRAISED, MY LORD, FOR OUR SISTER, MOTHER EARTH, WHO SUSTAINS AND KEEPS US AND WHO PRODUCES VARIED FRUITS, GRASS, AND COLORFUL FLOWERS.

BE PRAISED, MY LORD, FOR THOSE WHO FORGIVE FOR THE SAKE OF YOUR LOVE . . .

BE PRAISED BY THE WEAK AND SUFFERING.
BLESSED ARE THOSE WHO ENDURE IN PEACE,
FOR BY YOU, MOST HIGH, THEY WILL BE CROWNED.

BE PRAISED, MY LORD, FOR OUR SISTER DEATH,
FROM WHOM NO LIVING PERSON CAN ESCAPE.

BLESSED ARE THOSE WHOM SISTER DEATH FINDS DOING
YOUR MOST HOLY WILL,
FOR THEY WILL LIVE WITH YOU.

PRAISE AND BLESS MY LORD,
AND GIVE HIM THANKS;
SERVE THE LORD WITH GREAT HUMILITY.

THE SON OF PIETRO BERNARDONE

BORN IN ASSISI, ITALY, FRANCIS WAS THE SON OF A RICH CLOTH MERCHANT, PIETRO DI BERNARDONE, AND HIS WIFE PICA.

PIETRO, MY HUSBAND, LOOK AT YOUR SON, WHO WAS BORN WHILE YOU WERE IN FRANCE. I HAD HIM BAPTIZED AND NAMED HIM JOHN.

JOHN, YOU SAY? NO! THE BOY WILL BE CALLED FRANCIS, IN HONOR OF FRANCE, WHERE I BECAME RICH!

TIME WENT BY, AND FRANCIS GREW UP. BLESSED WITH GREAT INTELLIGENCE, HE BECAME A MERCHANT LIKE HIS FATHER.

FRANCIS, HOWEVER, PREFERRED TO LIVE IN EXTRAVAGANCE. HE SPENT ALL HIS MONEY ON PARTIES AND A LIFE OF LUXURY.

HE WANTED TO BE ADMIRED BY ALL, TO WIN IN GAMES, TO HAVE HIS DREAMS COME TRUE, AND TO WEAR THE BEST CLOTHES.

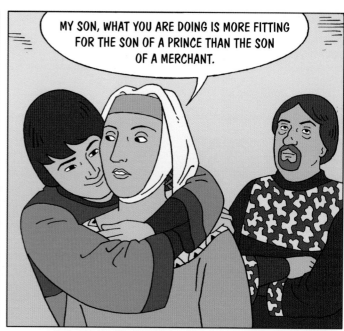

BUT FRANCIS DIDN'T PAY ANY ATTENTION TO HIS PARENTS. HE ROAMED THE STREETS OF TOWN NIGHT AND DAY WITH HIS FRIENDS DOING WHATEVER THEY WANTED.

ONE DAY, WHEN FRANCIS WAS BUSY IN THE SHOP, A BEGGAR CAME IN ASKING FOR MONEY.

FOR THE LOVE OF GOD, CAN YOU SPARE SOME CHANGE?

NO, DON'T BOTHER ME NOW . . .

IF THAT MAN HAD ASKED ME TO GIVE ANYTHING IN ORDER TO HELP A PRINCE OR A KING, I WOULD HAVE DONE IT. WITH MUCH MORE REASON I SHOULD HAVE DONE IT FOR THE KING OF KINGS, THE LORD OF ALL.

HEY!

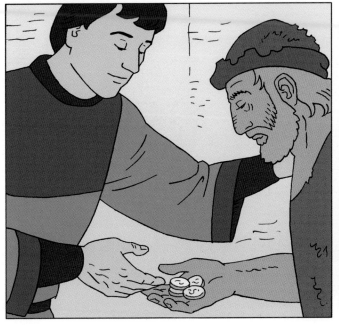

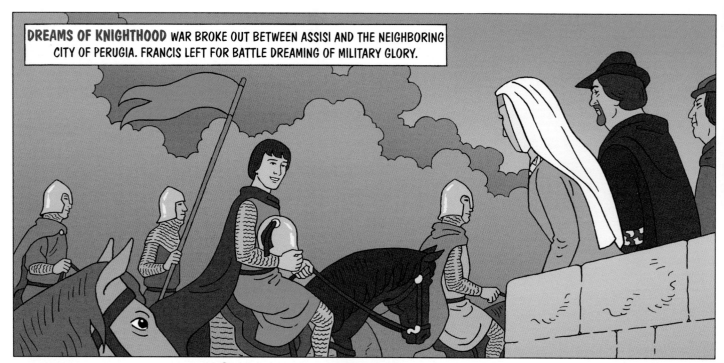

DREAMS OF KNIGHTHOOD WAR BROKE OUT BETWEEN ASSISI AND THE NEIGHBORING CITY OF PERUGIA. FRANCIS LEFT FOR BATTLE DREAMING OF MILITARY GLORY.

DURING THE BATTLE, FRANCIS WAS CAPTURED WITH OTHER MEN. HE SPENT HIS TIME THERE REACHING OUT TO THE OTHER PRISONERS.

FRANCIS IS ALWAYS JOKING. ONLY A FOOL WOULD BE HAPPY ABOUT BEING IMPRISONED HERE.

HA, HA, HA!

HA, HA, HA!

HE'S EVEN NICE TO THAT MAN EVERYONE ELSE AVOIDS!

AFTER A YEAR IN PRISON, A WEAKENED FRANCIS WAS RELEASED.

HE RETURNED TO ASSISI AND WAS VERY SICK FOR A LONG TIME.

WITH TIME FRANCIS RECOVERED FROM HIS ILLNESS. BUT SOMETHING WITHIN HIM HAD CHANGED.

NOBLE KNIGHT, FOR THE LOVE OF CHRIST, PLEASE TAKE MY CLOTHES.

WHY AM I NOT HAPPY TO BE HOME? I USED TO LOVE JUST RIDING THROUGH THE COUNTRYSIDE.

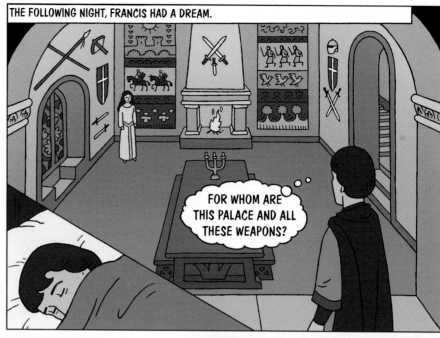

THE FOLLOWING NIGHT, FRANCIS HAD A DREAM.

FOR WHOM ARE THIS PALACE AND ALL THESE WEAPONS?

THIS IS ALL RESERVED FOR YOU, FRANCIS, AND FOR YOUR KNIGHTS.

NOW I KNOW! GOD WANTS ME TO BE A GREAT PRINCE. I'LL START BY BEING A KNIGHT SERVING THE COUNT.

FRANCIS HAD MISUNDERSTOOD THE DREAM. WHEN HE WOKE A VOICE HELPED HIM UNDERSTAND BETTER.

FRANCIS, IS IT BETTER TO SERVE THE MASTER OR THE SERVANT, THE RICH MAN OR THE POOR ONE?

THE MASTER.

WHY SEEK THE RICHES OF THE EARTH AND LEAVE BEHIND THE RICHES OF GOD?

LORD, WHAT SHOULD I DO?

GO HOME. I WILL MAKE CLEAR TO YOU WHAT YOU ARE TO DO.

BACK IN ASSISI, FRANCIS RESUMED HIS LIFE, BUT HE WAS NO LONGER INTERESTED IN ONLY HAVING FUN.

HEY, FRANCIS, WHAT ARE YOU THINKING ABOUT? ARE YOU THINKING ABOUT GETTING MARRIED?

YOU'RE RIGHT! I'M THINKING ABOUT MARRYING THE NOBLEST, RICHEST, AND MOST BEAUTIFUL LADY YOU'VE EVER SEEN.

HA, HA, HA!

HA, HA, HA!

HA, HA, HA!

FRANCIS PAID LESS AND LESS ATTENTION TO HIS FATHER'S BUSINESS. INSTEAD, HE WOULD OFTEN WITHDRAW TO A SOLITARY CAVE TO PRAY.

LEO, MY FRIEND, WAIT FOR ME HERE. I'M SEARCHING FOR A GREAT AND PRECIOUS TREASURE, BUT IT'S STILL HIDDEN AND I CAN'T FIND IT.

LORD, SHOW ME THE WAY. TEACH ME HOW TO FULFILL YOUR WILL.

THE CRUCIFIX OF SAN DAMIANO
ONE DAY, FRANCIS WAS RIDING A HORSE ACROSS THE PLAINS, WHEN SUDDENLY HE CAME UPON A MAN SUFFERING FROM LEPROSY.

I AM SO AFRAID OF CATCHING HIS ILLNESS. BUT IF I WANT TO BECOME A KNIGHT OF CHRIST, I MUST FIRST START BY CONQUERING MY FEAR. I WILL CHOOSE TO LOVE THIS MAN.

AS FRANCIS RODE ON HE CAME ACROSS AN OLD CHURCH THAT WAS FALLING APART. IT WAS THE CHURCH OF SAN DAMIANO.

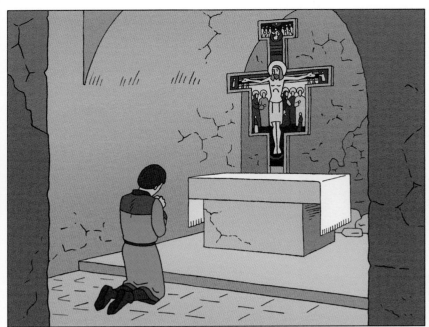

FRANCIS . . .

DO YOU NOT SEE THAT MY HOUSE IS IN RUINS? GO AND REBUILD IT FOR ME.

I WILL DO THAT WILLINGLY, MY LORD.

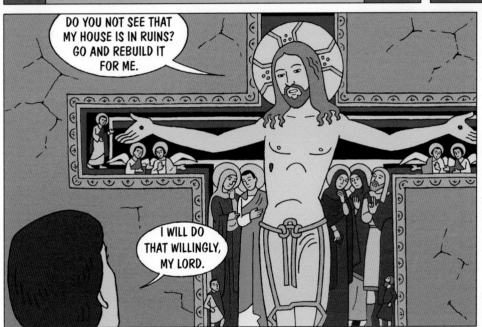

FIRST, I'LL GO TO THE NEARBY CITY TO SELL MY HORSE AND SOME FABRIC. THAT WAY I'LL HAVE THE MONEY TO FIX THE CHURCH OF SAN DAMIANO LIKE JESUS ASKED OF ME.

FATHER PETER, HERE IS THE MONEY FOR FIXING THE CHURCH. MAY I STAY HERE AT THE CHURCH FOR A LITTLE WHILE TO HELP REBUILD IT AND SO THAT I MAY SPEND TIME IN PRAYER?

ISN'T THIS FRANCIS, THE KING OF ASSISI'S PARTIES? I'D BETTER BE CAREFUL, OR ELSE HE MAY GET ME IN TROUBLE WITH HIS FATHER, PIETRO DI BERNARDONE.

YOU CAN STAY WITH ME, FRANCIS. BUT UNDER NO CONDITION WILL I ACCEPT THIS MONEY. WHAT WOULD YOUR FATHER SAY?

YOU DON'T WANT THE MONEY? NEITHER DO I!

WHEN HIS FATHER FOUND OUT THAT FRANCIS WAS STAYING WITH THE PRIEST AT SAN DAMIANO, PIETRO SENT FOR HIM. OUT OF FEAR FRANCIS HID IN A CAVE.

LORD, HELP MY FATHER TO UNDERSTAND THAT I WISH TO GIVE MYSELF TO YOU. GIVE ME THE GRACE TO DO YOUR WILL.

I HAVE BEEN A COWARD; I MUST RETURN IMMEDIATELY TO ASSISI.

LOOK! ISN'T THAT FRANCIS? HE, WHO THOUGHT HE WAS SUCH A BIG SHOT, HAS BECOME A FOOL!

YOUR FATHER WENT ON A TRIP. GO, MY SON, AND MAY GOD BLESS YOU!

FRANCIS QUICKLY RETURNED TO SAN DAMIANO TO CONTINUE REBUILDING THE CHURCH.

WHEN PIETRO DI BERNARDONE RETURNED, HE WAS ANGRY.

WHAT DO YOU MEAN YOU LET HIM GO? I'LL SHOW HIM WHO'S IN CHARGE AROUND HERE!

FATHER, I DON'T CARE ABOUT CHAINS AND BEING LOCKED UP. I'LL ENDURE ANYTHING FOR THE LOVE OF CHRIST.

GIVE ME BACK MY MONEY!

TAKE IT. IT'S STILL THERE, WHERE I LEFT IT.

THIS DOESN'T END HERE! I'LL SEE YOU BEFORE THE JUDGE!

BEGGING AND BUILDING
FRANCIS LEFT TOWN AND WALKED THROUGH THE FOREST SINGING GOD'S PRAISES.

YOU ARE HOLY, LORD GOD, WHO ALONE WORKS WONDERS. ♪

YOU ARE STRONG. YOU ARE GREAT. YOU ARE MOST HIGH. ♪

WHO ARE YOU?

I'M THE HERALD OF THE GREAT KING.

PLAF!

CRAC!

OW!

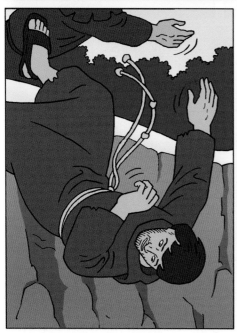

THAT'S WHERE YOU BELONG, MISERABLE HERALD OF GOD!

YOU ARE LOVE.
YOU ARE WISDOM.
YOU ARE HUMILITY.
YOU ARE PATIENCE.

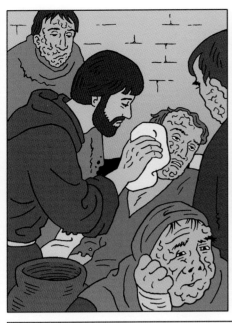

YOU ARE BEAUTY. YOU ARE MEEKNESS. YOU ARE SECURITY. YOU ARE TRANQUILITY . . .

WHOEVER GIVES ME ONE STONE WILL HAVE ONE REWARD; TWO STONES, TWO REWARDS; THREE STONES, A TRIPLE REWARD! ALL THIS IS FOR GOD!

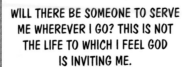

WILL THERE BE SOMEONE TO SERVE ME WHEREVER I GO? THIS IS NOT THE LIFE TO WHICH I FEEL GOD IS INVITING ME.

FROM NOW ON, PREPARE NO FOOD FOR ME. CHRIST WAS BORN POOR, LIVED IN THE POOREST WAY, REMAINED NAKED AND POOR UPON THE CROSS, AND WAS BURIED IN A BORROWED TOMB. FOR THE LOVE OF CHRIST I WILL LIVE AS A BEGGAR GOING FROM DOOR TO DOOR FOR EVERYTHING I NEED.

NOW THAT THE RESTORATION OF SAN DAMIANO IS FINISHED, IT WOULD BE NICE IF THE LAMPS WERE ALWAYS BRIGHTLY BURNING. I'LL GO TO ASSISI TO BEG FOR THE OIL THAT WILL BE NEEDED.

TOC! TOC!

THESE ARE MY OLD FRIENDS! I'LL BE SO EMBARRASSED IF THEY SEE ME BEGGING. I'LL KNOCK ON ANOTHER DOOR INSTEAD.

I CONFESS TO YOU, MY FRIENDS, THAT I WAS ASHAMED TO BEG AMONG YOU, BUT I WAS WRONG TO GIVE IN TO THAT FEELING. SO NOW I BEG YOU, FOR THE LOVE OF GOD, TO GIVE THE OIL NEEDED FOR THE LAMPS OF THE CHURCH OF SAN DAMIANO.

HERE IS THE ABANDONED CHAPEL OF SAINT MARY OF THE ANGELS. IT IS SO SMALL THAT THEY CALL IT THE PORTIUNCULA. NOW THAT SAN DAMIANO AND THE CHURCH OF SAINT PETER HAVE BEEN REPAIRED, I CAN WORK ON THIS ONE.

WHEN JESUS SENT THE TWELVE APOSTLES TO PREACH HE INSTRUCTED THEM: "TAKE NO GOLD, OR SILVER, OR COPPER IN YOUR BELTS, NO BAG FOR YOUR JOURNEY, OR TWO TUNICS, OR SANDALS . . ."
(MT 10:9-10).

WHAT JESUS TOLD HIS APOSTLES —THAT'S EXACTLY WHAT I DESIRE MOST!

THE FIRST FRIARS

FROM THEN ON, FRANCIS BEGAN TO SPREAD THE GOOD NEWS. HE PREACHED THE WORD OF GOD TO ALL THE MEN AND WOMEN WHO SOUGHT HIM OUT.

FRANCIS, IF SOMEONE HAD HIS MASTER'S GOODS AND DID NOT WANT THEM ANY LONGER, WHAT WOULD BE THE WISEST THING TO DO?

THAT PERSON SHOULD RETURN THOSE GOODS TO THE ORIGINAL OWNER.

IT IS I, BROTHER, WHO WANTS TO GIVE THE POOR ALL MY EARTHLY POSSESSIONS. I RECEIVED THEM FROM GOD. PLEASE DO WITH THEM WHAT YOU THINK IS BEST.

WE SHOULD ASK GOD WHAT TO DO, BERNARD. LET'S GO TO THE CHURCH AND PRAY THAT GOD WILL SHOW US WHAT HE DESIRES THROUGH HIS GOSPELS.

PLEASE, LET ME COME WITH YOU.

COME, THEN, PETER.

OH LORD, WE ARE SIMPLE PEOPLE, AS WE READ YOUR HOLY WORD, HELP US TO UNDERSTAND YOUR WILL.

"IF YOU WISH TO BE PERFECT, GO SELL YOUR POSSESSIONS, AND GIVE THE MONEY TO THE POOR" (MT 19:21).

"TAKE NOTHING FOR YOUR JOURNEY, NO STAFF, NOR BAG, NOR BREAD, NOR MONEY" (LK 9:3).

"IF ANY WANT TO BECOME MY FOLLOWERS, LET THEM DENY THEM- SELVES AND TAKE UP THEIR CROSS DAILY AND FOLLOW ME" (LK 9:23).

FOLLOWING THE ADVICE IN THE GOSPELS, BERNARD WENT OUT AND GAVE EVERYTHING AWAY.

FRANCIS, DO YOU REMEMBER ME? I'M FATHER SYLVESTER. YOU HAVE NOT YET PAID ME FOR THE STONES I SOLD YOU TO REPAIR THE CHURCH.

HAVE I PAID YOU WHAT I OWED YOU, FATHER?

YOU HAVE INDEED!

THAT EVENING . . .

I'M SO MISERABLE! I'M AN OLD MAN, STILL WORRIED ABOUT MONEY AND MERE THINGS, WHILE THOSE YOUNG MEN LEAVE THEM BEHND FOR THE LOVE OF GOD.

THE NEXT DAY . . .

WAIT FOR ME, BROTHER. I WANT TO JOIN YOU!

SOON OTHERS JOINED FRANCIS, TOO.

NOW GO AND ANNOUNCE PEACE. PREACH PENANCE FOR THE FORGIVENESS OF SINS TO ALL PEOPLE.

PUT YOUR TRUST IN THE LORD . . .

. . . FOR HE WILL SUSTAIN YOU.

MAY THE LORD GIVE YOU PEACE!

FOR A LONG TIME YOU HAVE CARRIED A SWORD AND SHIELD. FOLLOW ME AND YOU WILL BECOME A KNIGHT OF JESUS CHRIST.

AT SAINT MARY OF THE ANGELS, FRANCIS PRAYED THAT HIS COMPANIONS WOULD BE REUNITED SOON.

SOON THEY CAME TOGETHER, AND FOUR MORE COMPANIONS JOINED THEM! THERE WERE NOW TWELVE BROTHERS.

A VISIT TO THE POPE THE NUMBER OF BROTHERS CONTINUED TO INCREASE. THEY NEEDED TO KNOW HOW TO LIVE. SO FRANCIS WROTE A FEW SIMPLE LINES, CREATING A RULE OF LIFE FOR HIS DISCIPLES.

THEN HE LEFT FOR ROME TO OBTAIN THE POPE'S APPROVAL FOR THIS RULE OF LIFE.

FRANCIS, WHAT ARE YOU DOING IN ROME? ARE YOU ABANDONING OUR BELOVED ASSISI, WHERE THE LORD HAS DONE SUCH WONDERFUL DEEDS THROUGH ALL OF YOU?

DON'T WORRY, MY DEAR BISHOP OF ASSISI. WE HAVE COME TO OBTAIN POPE INNOCENT III'S APPROVAL OF OUR RULE OF LIFE.

YOUR WORDS REASSURE ME, FRANCIS! ALLOW ME TO INTRODUCE YOU TO MY FRIEND, CARDINAL JOHN. I HAVE TOLD HIM MUCH ABOUT YOU. HE CAN HELP YOU BRING YOUR CAUSE BEFORE THE POPE.

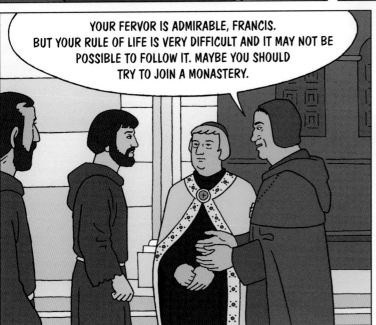

YOUR FERVOR IS ADMIRABLE, FRANCIS. BUT YOUR RULE OF LIFE IS VERY DIFFICULT AND IT MAY NOT BE POSSIBLE TO FOLLOW IT. MAYBE YOU SHOULD TRY TO JOIN A MONASTERY.

I MUST HUMBLY DECLINE YOUR ADVICE, CARDINAL. GOD IS CALLING US TO THIS LIFE.

IF THAT IS WHAT YOU WISH, I'LL HELP YOU GET AN AUDIENCE WITH THE POPE.

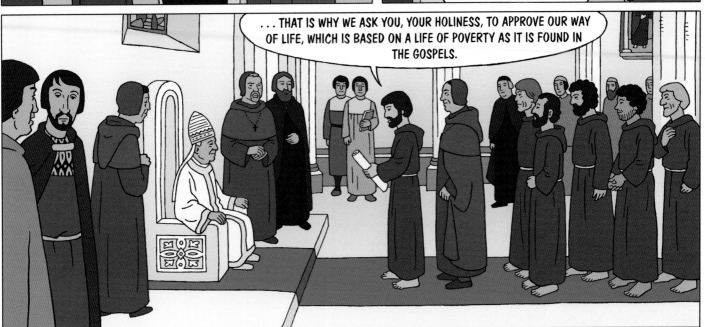

. . . THAT IS WHY WE ASK YOU, YOUR HOLINESS, TO APPROVE OUR WAY OF LIFE, WHICH IS BASED ON A LIFE OF POVERTY AS IT IS FOUND IN THE GOSPELS.

ALLOW ME TO POINT OUT, YOUR HOLINESS, THAT THE WAY OF LIFE FRANCIS AND HIS FOLLOWERS PROPOSE IS MOST UNUSUAL, AND VERY DIFFICULT.

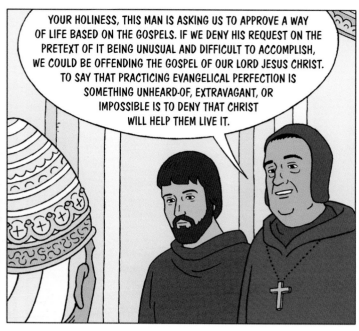

YOUR HOLINESS, THIS MAN IS ASKING US TO APPROVE A WAY OF LIFE BASED ON THE GOSPELS. IF WE DENY HIS REQUEST ON THE PRETEXT OF IT BEING UNUSUAL AND DIFFICULT TO ACCOMPLISH, WE COULD BE OFFENDING THE GOSPEL OF OUR LORD JESUS CHRIST. TO SAY THAT PRACTICING EVANGELICAL PERFECTION IS SOMETHING UNHEARD-OF, EXTRAVAGANT, OR IMPOSSIBLE IS TO DENY THAT CHRIST WILL HELP THEM LIVE IT.

MY SON, I SEE THE PURITY AND SIMPLICITY OF YOUR INTENTIONS, AS WELL AS YOUR DETERMINATION AND YOUR FERVENT DESIRE. NEVERTHELESS, I MUST PRAY AND ASK CHRIST TO MANIFEST HIS WILL. WHEN CHRIST'S WILL IS CLEAR TO ME, YOU WILL BE CALLED BACK.

THAT NIGHT, THE POPE HAD A DREAM.

28

TRULY, THIS IS THE MAN WHO, THROUGH HIS DEEDS AND HIS PREACHING, WILL SUPPORT THE CHURCH OF CHRIST.

GO WITH GOD, BROTHERS. FOLLOW THE INSPIRATIONS THE LORD WILL GIVE YOU AS YOU PREACH REPENTANCE TO ALL PEOPLE. MAY GOD INCREASE YOU IN NUMBER AND IN GRACE!

THE FRIARS' LIFE FRANCIS LIVED WITH HIS COMPANIONS NEAR ASSISI.

ONE ASCENDS TO HEAVEN QUICKER FROM THIS HUT THAN FROM A PALACE!

BROTHERS, OUR HOME IS SMALL AND POOR BUT EACH OF US HAS A PLACE HERE. I WILL WRITE OUR NAMES UPON THE BEAMS OF THIS HOUSE. THIS WAY WHOEVER WISHES TO REST OR TO PRAY WILL KNOW HIS SPOT.

I WANT OUR FRATERNITY TO BE CALLED THE ORDER OF THE FRIARS MINOR. GOD IS INVITING US TO BE SMALL, HUMBLE, AND TO PUT OTHERS AHEAD OF OURSELVES.

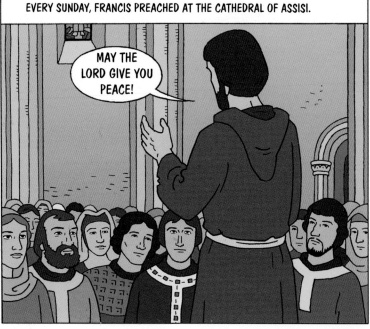

EVERY SUNDAY, FRANCIS PREACHED AT THE CATHEDRAL OF ASSISI.

MAY THE LORD GIVE YOU PEACE!

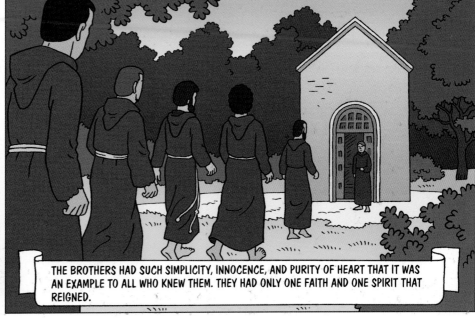

31

PREACHING TO THE BIRDS
AS THE ORDER KEPT GROWING, FRANCIS WAS UNSURE WHETHER TO DEVOTE HIMSELF TO PRAYER OR TO PREACHING.

GO TO SEE SISTER CLARE AND ASK HER TO PRAY THAT GOD MAKE HIS WILL KNOWN TO ME. SHOULD I DEDICATE MYSELF TO PREACHING OR TO PRAYER?

CLARE WAS FRANCIS'S FAVORITE DISCIPLE, AND SHE HAD FOUNDED THE ORDER OF POOR LADIES.

SHE BELONGED TO THE NOBILITY OF ASSISI. EVER SINCE SHE WAS A LITTLE GIRL, SHE HAD FELT A DEEP ATTRACTION TO THE IDEALS OF PRAYER AND POVERTY.

SHE EVEN RAN AWAY FROM HOME TO JOIN FRANCIS AND HIS COMPANIONS.

FRANCIS TOOK HER TO SAN DAMIANO, WHICH HE AND HIS FRIARS HAD PREPARED AS A HOME FOR CLARE AND THE YOUNG WOMEN THAT WOULD COME TO JOIN HER.

33

CHIRRRRP!

CHIRRRRP!

MAY THE PEACE OF THE LORD BE WITH YOU!

CHIRRRRP!

CHIRRRRP!

CHIRRRRP!

CHIRRRRP!

SISTER SWALLOWS, IT'S MY TURN TO TALK; YOU HAVE ALREADY SPOKEN ENOUGH. PLEASE BE QUIET UNTIL I HAVE FINISHED PREACHING.

CHIRRRRP!

AS IF THEY COULD UNDERSTAND, THE SWALLOWS IMMEDIATELY FELL SILENT.

WHERE THERE IS CHARITY AND WISDOM, THERE IS NEITHER FEAR NOR IGNORANCE. WHERE THERE IS PATIENCE AND HUMILITY, THERE IS NEITHER ANGER NOR ANXIETY.

WHERE THERE IS POVERTY WITH JOY, THERE IS NEITHER GREED NOR AVARICE. WHERE THERE IS PEACE AND TIME FOR CONTEMPLATION,

THERE IS NEITHER WORRY NOR WASTE. WHERE FEAR OF THE LORD GUARDS US, THERE THE ENEMY CANNOT ENTER. WHERE THERE IS MERCY AND PRUDENCE, THERE IS NEITHER CALLOUSNESS NOR RECKLESSNESS.

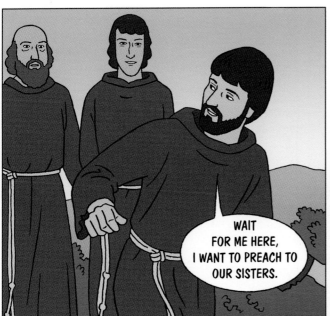

THE SULTAN OF EGYPT
FRANCIS THEN DECIDED TO UNDERTAKE HIS OWN CRUSADE TO THE HOLY LAND. HIS CRUSADE WOULD BE BASED ON PEACEFUL PREACHING AND NOT ON WAR OR FIGHTING.

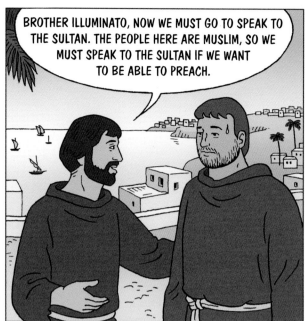

BROTHER ILLUMINATO, NOW WE MUST GO TO SPEAK TO THE SULTAN. THE PEOPLE HERE ARE MUSLIM, SO WE MUST SPEAK TO THE SULTAN IF WE WANT TO BE ABLE TO PREACH.

LET US TRUST IN THE LORD, BROTHER, BECAUSE WE ARE LIVING WHAT IT SAYS IN THE GOSPEL, "I AM SENDING YOU OUT LIKE SHEEP INTO THE MIDST OF WOLVES" (MT 10:16).

AH!

SULTAN! SULTAN!

YOU CALL FOR THE SULTAN? WHO ARE YOU?

LET'S JUST TAKE THEM BEFORE THE SULTAN.

TELL ME WHO SENT YOU AND WHY YOU WANT TO SEE ME.

THE ONE WHO SENDS US IS NOT AN EARTHLY MAN. IT IS GOD THE MOST HIGH, WHO SENDS US. HE WANTS US TO SHOW YOU THE ROAD TO SALVATION BY ANNOUNCING TO YOU THE GOSPEL OF CHRIST.

FRANCIS PREACHED TO THE SULTAN OF EGYPT WITH SUCH CONFIDENCE AND ENTHUSIASM THAT THE WORDS OF THE GOSPEL WERE FULFILLED, "I WILL GIVE YOU WORDS AND A WISDOM THAT NONE OF YOUR OPPONENTS WILL BE ABLE TO WITHSTAND OR CONTRADICT" (LK 21: 15).

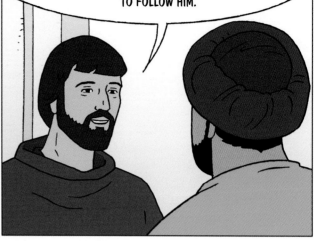

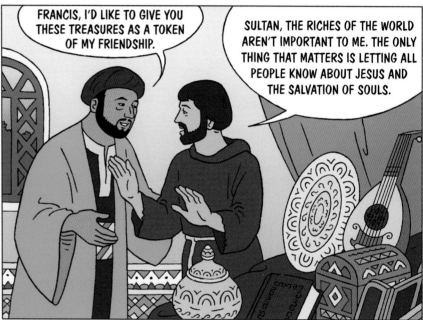

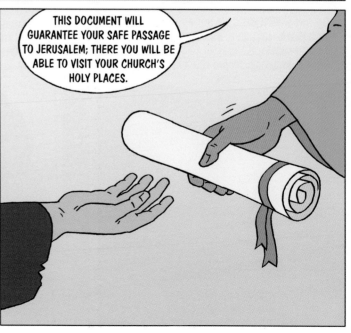

A FEW DAYS LATER . . .

BROTHER FRANCIS!

I JUST ARRIVED FROM SAINT MARY OF THE ANGELS TO BRING YOU NEWS! SOME WITHIN OUR GROUP ARE CAUSING TROUBLE. THE OTHER BROTHERS BEG YOU TO RETURN TO ITALY AS SOON AS POSSIBLE.

CHALLENGES FOR FRANCIS
WHEN FRANCIS RETURNED FROM JERUSALEM, THE FRIARS TOLD HIM ALL ABOUT THE PROBLEMS IN THE ORDER.

THE ORDER HAS BECOME SO BIG THAT NO ONE LISTENS TO THE FRIARS WHO WERE WITH YOU AT THE BEGINNING.

NOW THERE ARE MANY FRIARS WHO HAVE NEVER MET YOU!

THEY ARGUE THAT THE VOW OF POVERTY SHOULD BE LIVED LESS RIGOROUSLY. THEY ALSO WANT OUR HOMES TO BE MORE COMFORTABLE.

SOME DAYS LATER, ARRIVING AT SAINT MARY OF THE ANGELS, THE PORTIUNCULA......

OH NO! WHAT IS THIS?

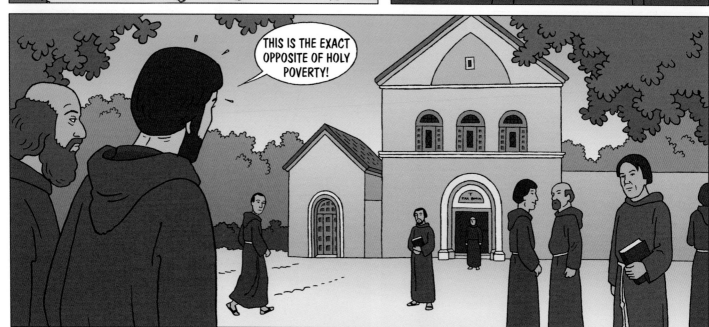

THIS IS THE EXACT OPPOSITE OF HOLY POVERTY!

BROTHERS, HELP ME!

DON'T YOU REALIZE THAT THIS MAJESTIC BUILDING GOES AGAINST THE VOW OF POVERTY? LATER OTHERS WILL THINK THEY HAVE TO IMITATE THIS!

STOP! BROTHER, THIS BUILDING BELONGS TO THE CITY OF ASSISI.

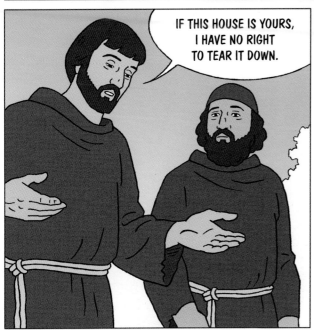

IF THIS HOUSE IS YOURS, I HAVE NO RIGHT TO TEAR IT DOWN.

THEY WANT US TO BE MORE LIKE MONASTIC ORDERS. SOME MONASTERIES ARE LIKE SCHOOLS WHERE THE FRIARS STUDY SO THAT THEIR PREACHING WILL BE MORE EFFECTIVE AND BRILLIANT.

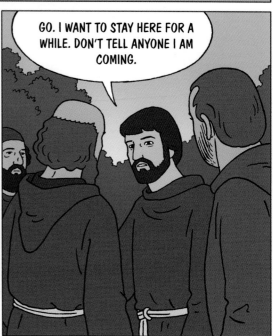

LATER . . .

WE BLESS YOU, LORD, FOR THIS FOOD . . .

ALMS FOR THE POOR, FOR THE LOVE OF GOD. I AM A POOR, SICK PILGRIM.

FOR THE LOVE OF OUR GOD WHOM YOU INVOKED, COME IN MY GOOD MAN.

BROTHER!

MAY I HAVE SOME SOUP, PLEASE?

NOW I AM A REAL BROTHER MINOR, A POOR MAN.

TRUE JOY
ONE DAY, WHILE WALKING, FRANCIS CALLED FOR BROTHER LEO.

BROTHER LEO, WRITE. I WILL TELL YOU WHAT TRUE JOY IS.

I AM READY.

IF A MESSENGER SHOULD ARRIVE ANNOUNCING THAT ALL THE GREAT TEACHERS FROM PARIS HAD COME INTO THE ORDER, THIS WOULD NOT BE TRUE JOY FOR US.

IF ALL THE BISHOPS, ARCHBISHOPS, AND EVEN THE KINGS OF FRANCE AND ENGLAND SHOULD JOIN THE ORDER, THIS WOULD NOT BE PERFECT JOY.

IF OUR BROTHERS GO TO THOSE WHO DO NOT BELIEVE IN GOD AND THEY WERE ALL TO BE CONVERTED TO THE FAITH, EVEN THAT IS NOT TRUE JOY.

IF I SHOULD HAVE SO MUCH GRACE FROM GOD THAT I AM ABLE TO HEAL THE SICK AND WORK MANY MIRACLES, I TELL YOU THAT TRUE JOY IS NOT FOUND THERE EITHER.

WHAT, THEN, IS PERFECT, TRUE JOY?

I REMEMBER ONE NIGHT . . . I ARRIVED HOME IN THE MIDDLE OF THE NIGHT . . . .

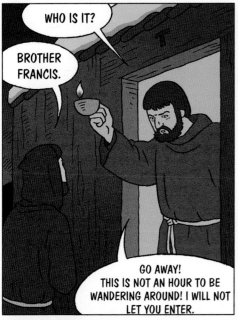

WOLF OF GUBBIO

WHEN FRANCIS LIVED IN THE CITY OF GUBBIO, THERE WAS A WOLF WHO ATE NOT ONLY OTHER ANIMALS BUT PEOPLE AS WELL! ALL THE INHABITANTS OF THE CITY LIVED IN GREAT FEAR OF THIS WOLF.

BECAUSE OF THE PEOPLE'S GREAT FEAR, FRANCIS WENT OUT TO MEET THE WOLF.

GRRR!

COME HERE, BROTHER WOLF. IN THE NAME OF CHRIST, I ORDER YOU TO DO NO HARM EITHER TO ME OR TO ANY OTHER PERSON.

BROTHER WOLF, YOU HAVE DONE MUCH HARM IN THIS REGION. I WANT TO MAKE PEACE BETWEEN YOU AND THE PEOPLE OF GUBBIO. IF YOU DON'T HURT THEM ANY MORE, THEY WILL FORGIVE EVERYTHING YOU HAVE DONE. THE MEN AND THE DOGS OF THE CITY WILL NO LONGER HUNT YOU DOWN.

I PROMISE YOU THAT THE PEOPLE OF GUBBIO WILL GIVE YOU FOOD EVERY DAY FOR AS LONG AS YOU LIVE. YOU'LL NEVER BE HUNGRY AGAIN. I KNOW THAT YOU ATTACKED ANIMALS AND PEOPLE BECAUSE YOU WERE HUNGRY. BUT, BROTHER WOLF, I WANT YOU TO PROMISE THAT YOU WILL NEVER AGAIN HURT ANY CREATURE OR PERSON. DO YOU PROMISE ME THIS?

THANK YOU, BROTHER WOLF! NOW COME WITH ME, WITHOUT FEAR, INTO GUBBIO.

BROTHER WOLF HAS PROMISED TO LIVE IN PEACE WITH YOU IF YOU PROMISE TO GIVE HIM SOME FOOD EVERY DAY. I PROMISE YOU THAT HE WILL KEEP THIS PACT.

AND YOU, BROTHER WOLF, WILL YOU PROMISE TO KEEP YOUR END OF THE AGREEMENT? PROMISE THE PEOPLE THAT YOU WON'T HURT ANY LIVING BEING AGAIN.

THE ONCE FEROCIOUS WOLF BECAME GENTLE AND LIVED IN GUBBIO FOR ANOTHER TWO YEARS UNTIL HE DIED OF OLD AGE. THE CITIZENS, WHO ALWAYS REMEMBERED THE HOLINESS OF FRANCIS, MOURNED THE WOLF'S DEATH GREATLY.

THE FIRST NATIVITY SCENE
THERE LIVED IN THE TOWN OF GRECCIO A MAN NAMED JOHN. HE WAS A FRIEND OF FRANCIS'S.

JOHN, WILL YOU HELP US TO PREPARE FOR A VERY SPECIAL CHRISTMAS IN GRECCIO THIS YEAR?

LET'S HELP EVERYONE REMEMBER THAT JESUS WAS BORN AS A POOR CHILD. HE SUFFERED DISCOMFORT AND WAS PLACED ON A BED OF STRAW IN A MANGER BETWEEN AN OX AND A DONKEY.

SAINT LUKE TELLS US THAT WHILE MARY AND JOSEPH WERE IN BETHLEHEM "THE TIME CAME FOR HER TO DELIVER HER CHILD."

"AND SHE GAVE BIRTH TO HER FIRSTBORN SON AND WRAPPED HIM IN BANDS OF CLOTH, AND LAID HIM IN A MANGER, BECAUSE THERE WAS NO PLACE FOR THEM IN THE INN" (LK 2:6-7).

THIS CHRISTMAS WE REMEMBER THAT JESUS OUR KING WAS NOT BORN IN A FANCY PALACE. INSTEAD, HE CHOSE TO BE BORN POOR AND LIVED HIS ENTIRE LIFE THIS WAY. IN LIVING SIMPLY AS HE DID WE CAN UNDERSTAND THAT THINGS ARE NOT SO IMPORTANT. WHAT MATTERS MOST IS WHAT WE TREASURE IN OUR HEARTS.

OUR HUMBLE LORD CAME NOT TO CONDEMN US BUT TO GIVE US LIFE, LIFE EVERLASTING.

THIS CHRISTMAS LET US THANK GOD FOR THE GIFT OF BEING ABLE TO LIVE AS JESUS DID. MAY WE LOVE GOD AND LOVE ONE ANOTHER. MAY WE, LIKE JESUS BRING GOD'S MESSAGE OF PEACE AND LOVE TO ALL PEOPLE.

THE MARKS OF CHRIST

TWO YEARS BEFORE HE DIED, FRANCIS WITHDREW, AS WAS HIS CUSTOM, TO THE MOUNTAIN OF ALVERNA IN ORDER TO ENTER INTO DEEPER PRAYER AND CONTEMPLATION. AFTER SOME DAYS ON THE ROAD, HE WAS SO EXHAUSTED THAT HE ASKED A PEASANT TO LEND HIM A DONKEY TO RIDE.

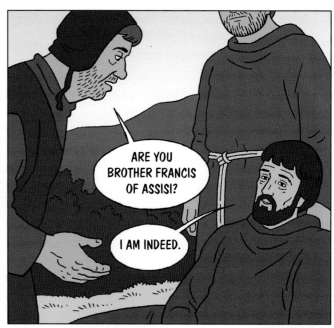

ARE YOU BROTHER FRANCIS OF ASSISI?

I AM INDEED.

THEN TRY TO BE AS GOOD AS PEOPLE BELIEVE YOU ARE!

THANK YOU, BROTHER, FOR YOUR KIND ADVICE.

A FEW DAYS LATER . . .

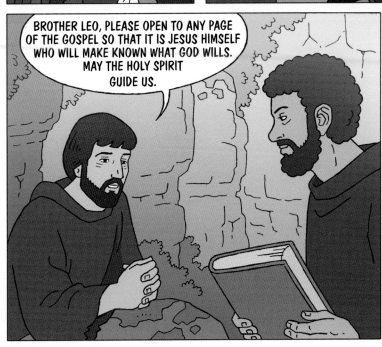

BROTHER LEO, PLEASE OPEN TO ANY PAGE OF THE GOSPEL SO THAT IT IS JESUS HIMSELF WHO WILL MAKE KNOWN WHAT GOD WILLS. MAY THE HOLY SPIRIT GUIDE US.

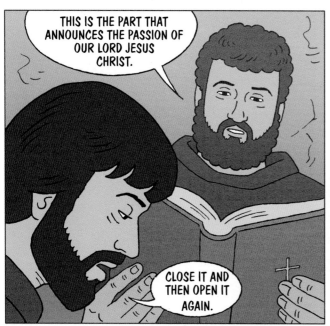

THIS IS THE PART THAT ANNOUNCES THE PASSION OF OUR LORD JESUS CHRIST.

CLOSE IT AND THEN OPEN IT AGAIN.

IT IS THE STORY OF THE PASSION OF CHRIST.

OPEN IT A THIRD TIME, IN THE NAME OF THE MOST HOLY TRINITY.

THE PASSION.

I UNDERSTAND WHAT THE LORD IS TELLING ME. SINCE I HAVE SOUGHT TO IMITATE CHRIST IN MY LIFE, BEFORE I DIE I WILL EXPERIENCE SOME OF HIS SUFFERING.

LORD, GRANT ME TWO GRACES BEFORE I DIE: THAT I MAY FEEL IN MY BODY AND SOUL THE PAINS YOU SUFFERED DURING YOUR PASSION; AND THAT I MAY FEEL IN MY HEART THE LOVE YOU FELT WHICH LED YOU TO SACRIFICE YOURSELF FOR US.

GOD ALLOWED FRANCIS TO RECEIVE THE STIGMATA, THE WOUNDS THAT JESUS BORE DURING HIS CRUCIFIXION.

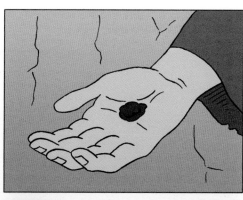

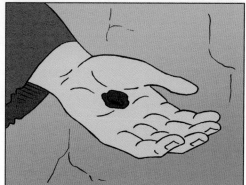

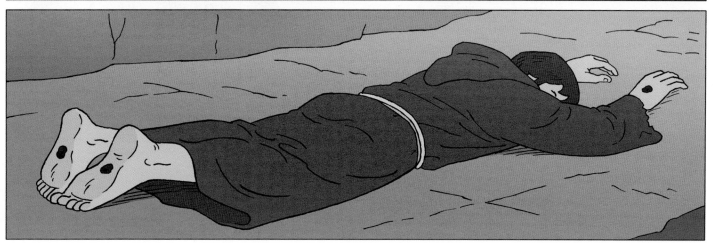

THE LAST GOODBYE

FRANCIS LIVED WITH THE PAINFUL STIGMATA FOR THE LAST TWO YEARS OF HIS LIFE. HE GREW WEAKER AND HE CONTRACTED A GRIEVOUS AILMENT IN HIS EYES.

BROTHER FRANCIS, I AM BROTHER ELIAS, THE MINISTER GENERAL YOU CHOSE TO LEAD OUR ORDER. I COMMAND YOU TO GO TO RIETI WHERE THERE IS A DOCTOR WHO IS A SPECIALIST REGARDING DISEASES OF THE EYE.

BROTHERS, MAY WE PLEASE STOP AT SAN DAMIANO? I WANT TO SAY GOODBYE TO CLARE.

SISTER CLARE, BROTHER FRANCIS IS VERY ILL.

FRANCIS ASKED THAT A HUT MADE OF REEDS BE PREPARED IN THE CONVENT GARDEN, JUST LIKE THE ONE HE USED TO STAY IN AT SAINT MARY OF THE ANGELS.

LORD, HELP ME TO BEAR MY ILLNESSES WITH PATIENCE.

FRANCIS, IF THE EARTH AND ALL THE UNIVERSE WERE MADE OF THE PUREST GOLD AND YOU KNEW THAT ALL THIS TREASURE IS WORTHLESS IN COMPARISON TO THE REWARD YOU WILL RECEIVE FOR THE SUFFERINGS YOU BEAR, IS IT NOT TRUE THAT YOU WOULD BE HAPPY TO ENDURE THEM?

YES, LORD, I'D BE VERY HAPPY!

IN SPITE OF THE DOCTOR'S TREATMENT, FRANCIS'S VARIOUS ILLNESSES WORSENED. REALIZING THAT HIS TIME ON EARTH WAS DRAWING TO AN END, HE ASKED HIS BROTHERS TO TAKE HIM BACK TO SAINT MARY OF THE ANGELS.

WHEN YOU SEE THAT I AM AT THE POINT OF DEATH, REMOVE MY HABIT AND LAY ME DOWN ON THE BARE GROUND OF THE CHAPEL.

I HAVE COMPLETED MY MISSION.

MAY CHRIST NOW SHOW YOU YOUR MISSION.

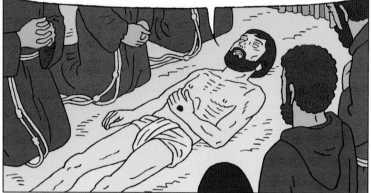

BE PRAISED, MY LORD, FOR OUR SISTER DEATH, FROM WHOM NO LIVING PERSON CAN ESCAPE.

WHEN FRANCIS PASSED AWAY, GREAT FLOCKS OF LARKS ARRIVED AND CIRCLED OVER SAINT MARY OF THE ANGELS FOR A LONG TIME.

FRANCIS DIED ON OCTOBER 4, 1226.
HE WAS DECLARED A SAINT ON JULY 16, 1228.

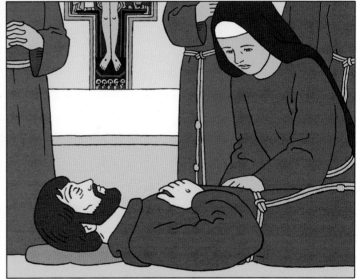

PRAYER FOR PEACE

LORD, MAKE ME AN INSTRUMENT OF YOUR PEACE.

WHERE THERE IS HATRED,

LET ME BRING LOVE.

WHERE THERE IS DISCORD,

LET ME BRING UNITY.

WHERE THERE IS INJURY,

LET ME BRING PARDON.

WHERE THERE IS DESPAIR,

LET ME BRING HOPE.

WHERE THERE IS DOUBT,

LET ME BRING FAITH.

WHERE THERE IS DARKNESS, MAY I BRING LIGHT.

WHERE THERE IS SADNESS, MAY I BRING JOY.

O LORD, GRANT THAT I MAY NOT SO MUCH SEEK TO BE CONSOLED AS TO CONSOLE; TO BE UNDERSTOOD, AS TO UNDERSTAND; TO BE LOVED, AS TO LOVE.

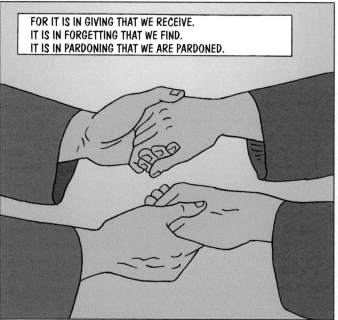

FOR IT IS IN GIVING THAT WE RECEIVE. IT IS IN FORGETTING THAT WE FIND. IT IS IN PARDONING THAT WE ARE PARDONED.

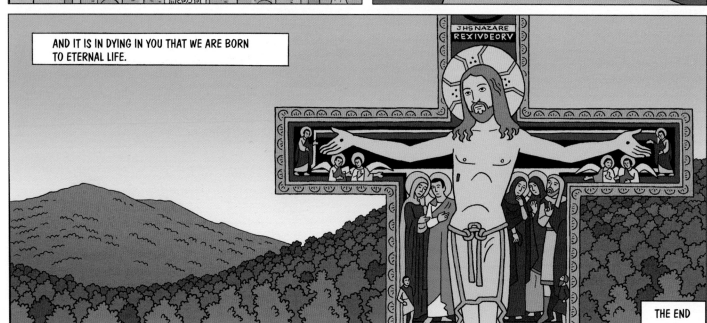

AND IT IS IN DYING IN YOU THAT WE ARE BORN TO ETERNAL LIFE.

THE END

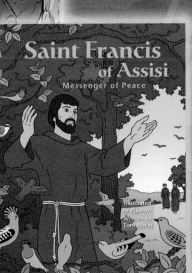

Courage
Commitment
Compassion

These are just some of the qualities
of the saints you'll find in our popular
Encounter the Saints series.
Join Saint Ignatius, Saint Isaac,
Saint Kateri, and many other holy
men and women as they discover
and try to do what God asks of them.
Get swept into the exciting and
inspiring lives of the Church's heroes
and heroines while encountering the
saints in a new and fun way!

Collect all the
Encounter the Saints
books by visiting
www.pauline.org.

Saint Isaac Jogues
With Burning Heart

by Christine Virginia
Orfeo, FSP and Mary
Elizabeth Tebo, FSP

Saint Kateri Tekakwitha
Courageous Faith

Adapted from a book
by Lillian M. Fisher

Saint Francis of Assisi
Gentle Revolutionary

by Mary Emmanuel Alves, FSP